D1191653

F
B

CARDINALS
IN THE PINE

Text and Photographs by LORENZ BOYD

DRAWINGS BY CORNELIA BROWN

Nashville   **ABINGDON PRESS**   New York

HILBERT COLLEGE
Learning Resources Center
5200 South Park Avenue
Hamburg, ew ork 075

26,940

Copyright © 1969 by Abingdon Press
All Rights Reserved
Printed in the United States of America
Library of Congress Catalog Card Number 69-10612

For
LaVelle

David could not believe his eyes. "Dad! Mom!" he called. "Come look at this."

It was the last Saturday in April. David had looked out to see if any of his friends were playing baseball on the vacant lot across the street. He stood on tiptoe at the window to get a better view through the branches of a pine tree which grew beside his house.

This morning there was no one playing ball, but there was something in the pine tree— something new.

"Hurry, hurry," David called again.

5

"What is it, David?" His parents came running into his room.

"Look, just look," David said, "a bird has built a nest in the pine."

Only a few feet outside the window on a trim little nest in the tree sat a gray bird with dull red wings, dull red crest, and a bright orange bill.

"Why, it's a cardinal," David's father said.

David shook his head. "I don't think so, Dad. Cardinals are bright red, not gray."

David felt sure about that. His class at school had been studying birds. He knew the cardinal was red, the only red bird with a crest.

"The male cardinal is red," said David's

father, "but the mother is a dull color like the bird on the nest. If we were farther away it would be hard to see her there. Her color helps her hide from larger birds that might steal the eggs from her nest."

David's mother put her finger to her lips and said, "Shhh. Listen."

As they stood very still, all of them heard what David's mother had heard a moment before. There were several shrill whistles that sounded like *wheeet, wheeet, wheeeet.* The sounds came from a maple tree in the yard.

"I see it, I see it," David cried, forgetting to keep still. He could see the bright red male cardinal on a limb in the maple tree across the yard from the pine.

"Yes, there he is," David's father said, and his mother nodded her head.

With almost the same *wheeet, wheeet, wheeeet* the cardinal on the nest answered the call. Then she hopped to another limb in the pine, waited a moment, and flew from there to meet her mate in the maple tree.

David's father chuckled. "It's time for the mother cardinal's breakfast," he said. As they watched, the male bird placed what appeared to be a small insect in his mate's bill. "While the mother cardinal nests, her mate finds food for her," Father explained.

David's mother had seen something else. "Look in the nest," she whispered.

The cardinal's nest was built of twigs and was lined with soft grass. It was anchored safely at the fork of a limb. In the nest were three eggs.

"I wish we could see the eggs closer," David said.

10

His father thought for a moment. "Maybe you can," he said, and he left the room for a moment. When he returned he had a camera and a very long lens.

David's father was a photographer for a newspaper.

"This is a telephoto lens," he said to David. "It is much like a telescope. When you look into the camera it will be like looking through a small telescope."

David looked into the camera. The cardinal's eggs appeared so close he felt he could reach out and touch them. They were light blue, spotted with brown.

David's father and mother looked through the camera, and then David looked again. As he looked, the mother cardinal flew back to the pine tree. She landed on a limb above the nest, then hopped down to it, rustled her feathers, and settled gently on the eggs.

At school on Monday morning David told his teacher about the nest in the pine tree.

"There are three eggs in it," he said, "and the father brings food to the mother. But not when she is in the pine tree. He calls to her from the maple tree and she flies over there to eat."

Miss Morton, the teacher, asked David to tell the whole class about the nest. His friends asked many questions.

"Why doesn't the male cardinal bring his mate's food to her at her nest?" someone wanted to know.

"How long will it take the eggs to hatch?"

"When do baby birds learn to fly?"

There were many questions, and David did not know all the answers.

"I have an idea," Miss Morton said. "In the school library I will find a book for David to read. David can help us learn the answers."

The book Miss Morton found for David was all about birds, many kinds of birds. He could hardly wait to start reading.

"David," Miss Morton said, "there is something else you must do. The nest is beside your window. You will have a chance to watch a cardinal family grow right before your eyes. You may learn something that is not in the book. The

14

class will want to hear about what you see each day, especially after the eggs hatch."

Everyone clapped. The whole class liked Miss Morton's idea.

David's mother and father were glad to hear about the project Miss Morton had given him. After dinner that evening David looked at the book about birds. He told his mother and father some of the things he had learned.

"Did you know," David asked his parents, "that the cardinal is one of the favorite birds in the United States? Some people may think it lives only in the South, but it is found as far north as Canada.

"And there's something else I'll bet you didn't know. The cardinal is the state bird of seven states—Ohio, Illinois, Indiana, Kentucky, North Carolina, Virginia, and West Virginia."

Illinois
Indiana
Kentucky
North Carolina
Ohio
Virginia
West Virginia

17

From the book David learned another thing: some cardinal eggs are blue and brown, others are white and brown. They hatch in fourteen days. Because he did not know exactly when the eggs were laid in the pine tree, David could not be sure when they would hatch. He would watch each day.

One day while David was watching the mother on the nest, he heard the male cardinal calling *wheet, wheeet, wheeeet.*

"Good," thought David. "The mother bird will go to get her dinner, and I can see if the eggs have hatched."

The mother cardinal did not answer her mate's call. The bright red male called again and again, but still the mother did not reply.

She stayed on the nest, very quiet, very still.

David, watching silently, saw the male cardinal fly out and away from the maple tree. From the top of the pine there came a sound of wings fluttering. David looked up to see a large bluejay.

Then he knew why the mother cardinal had not answered her mate. There was danger. The bluejay might rob the nest if he knew the eggs were there.

"And that," said David to himself, "is why the male cardinal never comes to the nest. His feathers are so flashy he could be seen easily by other birds."

Many days passed. David began to wonder if the eggs were going to hatch at all.

One Saturday morning, two weeks after he first saw the nest, David was awakened by the male cardinal's familiar call. *Wheeet. Wheeeet. Wheeeet.*

David's window was open now, for the days and nights were getting warmer. When he heard the mother cardinal's answer, David moved quietly to the window. Today there was something very special to see.

The mother bird was on a limb just above the nest. In the nest were three pink baby cardinals. The babies were so funny to see! David held his hand over his mouth to keep from laughing aloud and frightening the mother.

The baby cardinals had no feathers. They had fuzzy puffs of soft gray down on their heads, wings, and backs, and their heads appeared as large as their round little bodies. Their eyes were closed but they were very large.

Suddenly the male cardinal flew into the pine tree. Now that the eggs were hatched the male could risk being seen near the nest. David saw there was an insect in the male's bill. He flew right to the nest, and when he arrived there three pink little heads lifted upward on long thin necks.

As David watched, the father bird poked an insect into first one baby's mouth and then another until each of the little birds had been fed. Then the male cardinal flew away to look for more food for his hungry family.

And then David saw the mother cardinal hop back down to the nest. The little heads raised up and the mouths popped open again. The mother bird checked the throat of each of her babies.

From the book Miss Morton had given him, David knew that baby birds will eat as much as they are given. If they eat more than their stomachs can hold, the food may stay in their throats and choke them. Now the mother cardinal in the pine tree removed some of the food from her babies' throats so they were safe.

David's mother and father came to the window to watch the new cardinal family. About every fifteen minutes the father bird arrived with more food and fed the babies. After each feeding the mother checked the little throats.

David's father brought his camera to the

F
B
26,940

window again so they could look at the baby birds through the telephoto lens.

The next day David's father placed a ladder beside the pine tree, and David climbed up for a closer look at the babies when the mother and father cardinals were away for a few moments. He knew he must not touch the nest. That would leave a human scent and might cause the mother and father birds to desert their babies.

David found he could get the little birds to raise their heads and open their mouths if he gently shook the limb that held the nest. "This must be how the father and mother get the babies to open their mouths for food," David whispered to his father. His father agreed that the motion of the nest was the signal to the baby birds to open their mouths.

25

HILBERT COLLEGE
Learning Resources Center
5200 South Park Avenue
Hamburg, New York 14075

The following Monday was an exciting day at school.

"Miss Morton," David began, "they're here. They have the longest necks, but they are so little!"

"Start over, David," Miss Morton said. "What is so little?"

"The eggs have hatched! There are three baby cardinals. I saw the father feed them. At first there was a big bluejay up in the tree but he went away—"

There was such a lot to tell about what he had seen on Saturday. All the boys and girls asked questions, and David tried to answer them. Several times he had to say, "I'll look it up in the book and tell you tomorrow."

David hurried home from school. When he looked at the nest in the pine tree there was another surprise. The baby cardinals had their eyes open!

The next morning David saw that feathers were beginning to appear on the baby birds where before only gray down had been. And there was something else—the little cardinals were getting their voices. They began to squeak at feeding time, which now was about every half hour.

By the time the babies were a week old,

they had many feathers. They were gray like their mother.

David knew they would be nearly two months old before the male cardinals would turn red. Their voices were much louder now, and David had to close his window at night so he could sleep through their noisy feeding times.

Each evening David and his father looked at the cardinals through the camera with its telephoto lens. The next day at school David could tell his friends all the changes he saw in the little birds.

Then, when the cardinals were ten days old, David came home and rushed to the window for a quick look. The nest was empty! David started to call out to his mother, but he stopped just in time. He made no sound, for he had discovered

the cardinals were still in the pine tree. Each of
the babies was on a separate limb. And that was
not all. As David watched, the little birds fluttered
and flew from limb to limb for very short distances.

By the next morning the baby cardinals were in other trees in the yard. Each baby had gone to a different tree. The father cardinal still found them by calling to them and waiting for their squeaking reply. But David knew the little birds would never return to the nest in the pine.

"I will miss those cardinals," David said at breakfast.

"So will I," said his mother, "but we were very lucky to be able to watch them grow."

David's father smiled. "And we can remember them always." He put a big gray envelope on the table. "This will help us remember them."

David opened the envelope. "Pictures!" he shouted. "Pictures of our cardinals."

"I thought," said his father, "that as long as we were looking through the camera, the camera might as well help us remember them."

"Just look at this one," David began and then stopped. "May I take these to school to show Miss Morton and the others?"

"Of course," said his father. "Let everybody look and enjoy them."

"I'm going right this minute," David cried.

"Tie your sneakers," called his mother, but David was already out the front door.

"Look, Miss Morton," David called as he went running into his classroom. "I have pictures of the cardinals. My father made them when we were looking through the big lens on his camera."

All the children crowded around to see the cardinal family.

"These are the eggs when I saw them the first day," explained David.

36

"Here is a picture of the mother cardinal on the nest," said Miss Morton.

"What is *that*?" asked one boy.

"That," said David, "is a picture of the babies before they opened their eyes. Don't their eyes look like big gray knots?"

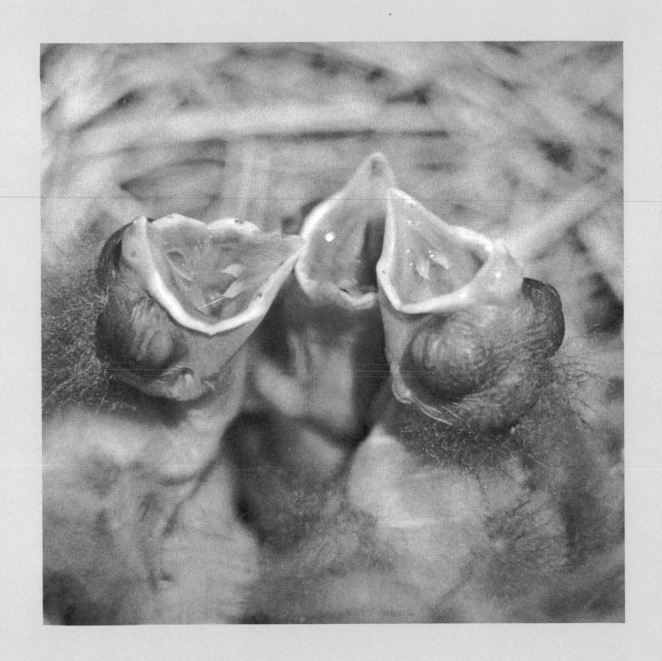

"You will remember that for the first few days, the father cardinal came about every fifteen minutes to feed the babies," Miss Morton explained, "and here is a picture of one of those times."

42

"This one," said David, "shows the babies waiting to be fed. They were about four days old. The next day they began to squeak at feeding time. You could hear them almost a block away."

"Look," said Miss Morton, "look at this picture of the mother checking their throats after the father has fed them."

44

"When they were about eleven days old they flew to other trees," David said sadly, "but we could hear them squeaking at feeding time. My father was able to get this picture of one of the babies when he came back to the pine tree one day. It looks like its mother now, but if it is a male it will begin to turn red in about two months."

"David," said Miss Morton, "why don't you write a story about your cardinals?"

"A story? What would I call the story?"

"Cardinals in the Pine," the other children shouted.

"That's a good idea," David said, and he smiled happily.